Sax After Midnight Wonderful Tonight...

Wise Publications
London/New York/Paris/Sydney/Copenhagen/Madrid

Exclusive Distributors:
Music Sales Limited
8-9 Frith Street, London W1V 5TZ, England.
Music Sales Pty Limited
120 Rothschild Avenue, Rosebery, NSW 2018,
Australia.

Order No. AM954888
ISBN 0-7119-7474-8
This book © Copyright 1999 by Wise Publications

Compiled by Jack Long
New music engravings by
Enigma Music Production Services
Cover design by Studio Twenty, London

Printed in the United Kingdom by
Caligraving Limited, Thetford, Norfolk.

Your Guarantee of Quality
As publishers, we strive to produce every book to
the highest commercial standards.
This book has been carefully designed to minimise
awkward page turns and to make playing from it a real
pleasure. Particular care has been given to specifying
acid-free, neutral-sized paper made from pulps which
have not been elemental chlorine bleached. This pulp
is from farmed sustainable forests and was produced
with special regard for the environment.
Throughout, the printing and binding have been
planned to ensure a sturdy, attractive publication
which should give years of enjoyment.
If your copy fails to meet our high standards,
please inform us and we will gladly replace it.

Music Sales' complete catalogue describes thousands
of titles and is available in full colour sections by
subject, direct from Music Sales Limited. Please
state your areas of interest and send a cheque/postal
order for £1.50 for postage to: Music Sales Limited,
Newmarket Road, Bury St. Edmunds,
Suffolk IP33 3YB.

www.internetmusicshop.com

Baker Street

Words & Music by Gerry Rafferty

Blues In The Night
(My Mama Done Tol' Me)

Words by Johnny Mercer
Music by Harold Arlen

Blues tempo

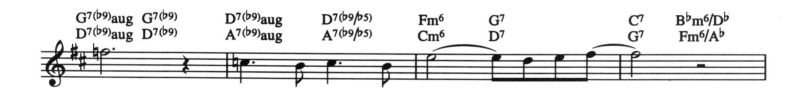

D. $ al Coda

7

The Best Is Yet To Come

Words by Carolyn Leigh
Music by Cy Coleman

Medium swing

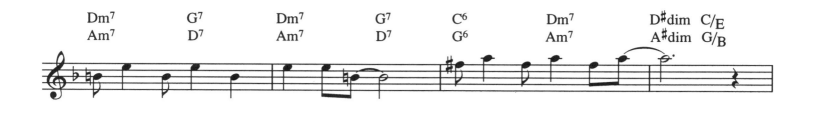

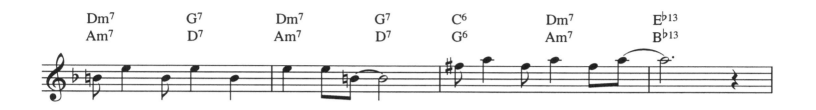

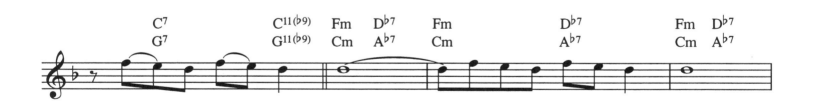

9

Cry Me A River

Words & Music by Arthur Hamilton

Don't Dream Of Anybody But Me
(Li'l Darlin')

Words by Bart Howard
Music by Neal Hefti

CODA

13

For All We Know

Words by Robb Wilson & Arthur James
Music by Fred Karlin

Medium fast (Lyrically)

Just The Two Of Us

Words & Music by Ralph MacDonald,
William Salter & Bill Withers

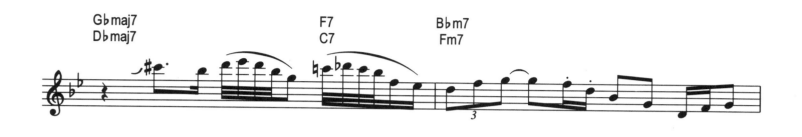

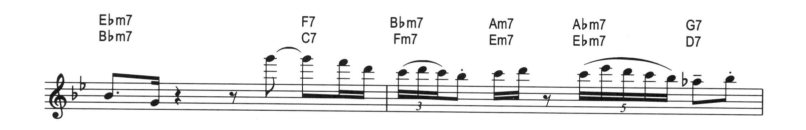

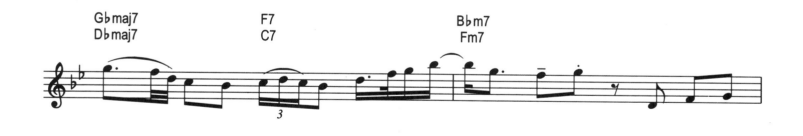

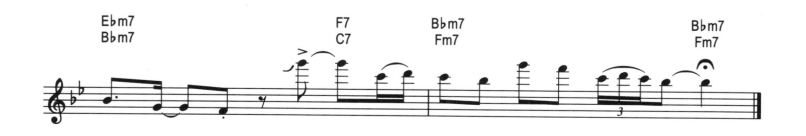

In A Sentimental Mood

Words & Music by Duke Ellington, Irving Mills & Manny Kurtz

The Lady Sings The Blues

Words by Billie Holiday
Music by Herbie Nichols

Learnin' The Blues

Words & Music by Dolores Vicki Silvers

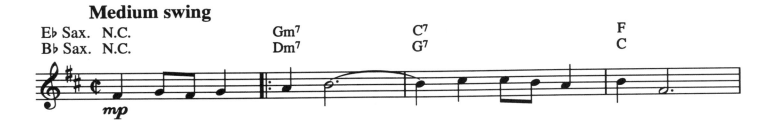

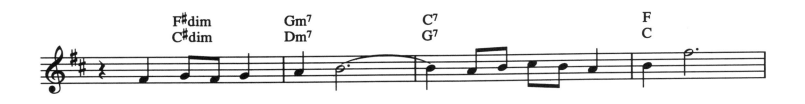

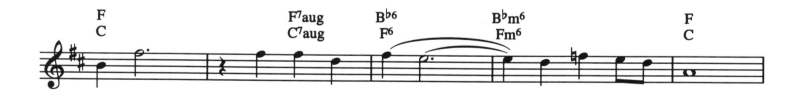

21

Lullaby of Birdland

Music by George Shearing
Words by George David Weiss

Meditation (Meditaçao)

Original Words by Newton Mendonca.
English Lyric by Norman Gimbel. Music by Antonio Carlos Jobim

Midnight Sun

Words by Johnny Mercer
Music by Sonny Burke & Lionel Hampton

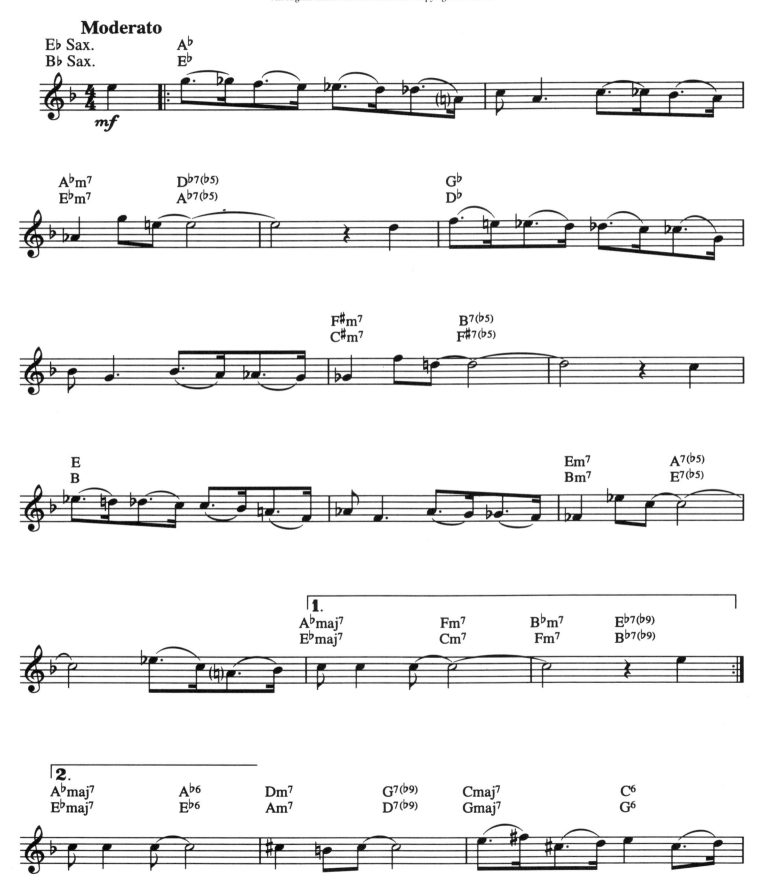

Moonlight Becomes You

Music by Jimmy Van Heusen
Words by Johnny Burke

One For My Baby
(And One More For The Road)

Words by Johnny Mercer
Music by Harold Arlen

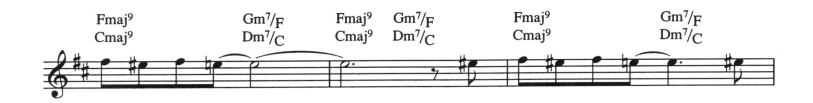

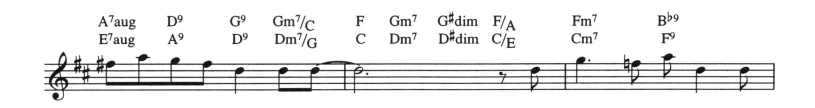

Recado Bossa Nova (The Gift)

Words & Music by Djalma Ferreira & Luiz Antonio

Bossa nova

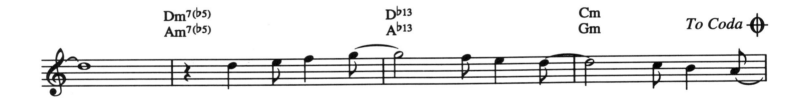

CODA

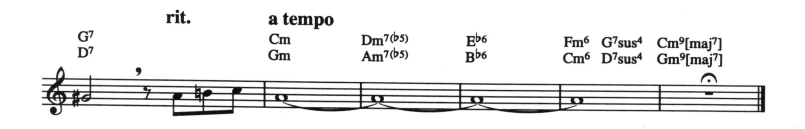

Round Midnight

By Cootie Williams & Thelonious Monk

33

Slightly Out Of Tune (Desafinado)

English Lyric by Jon Hendricks & Jessie Cavanaugh
Music by Antonio Carlos Jobim

Smoke Gets In Your Eyes

Music by Jerome Kern
Words by Otto Harbach

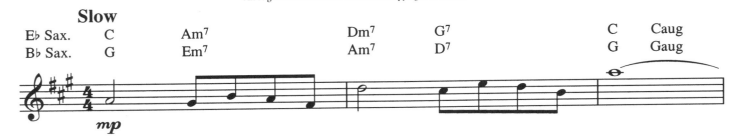

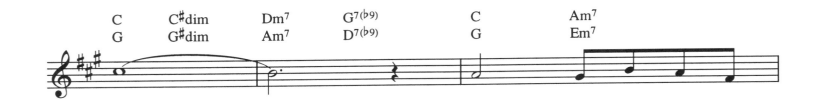

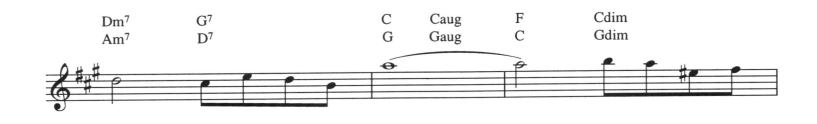

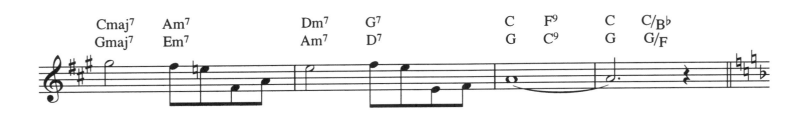

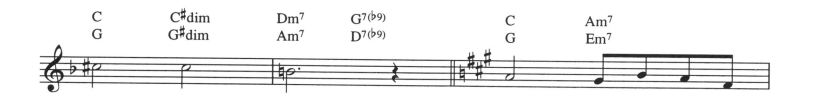

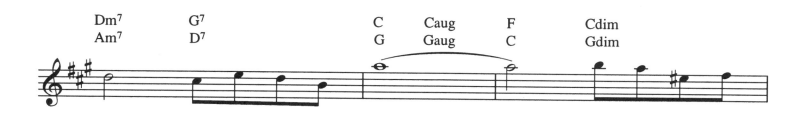

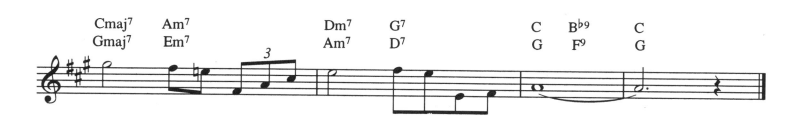

Solitaire

Words & Music by Philip Cody & Neil Sedaka

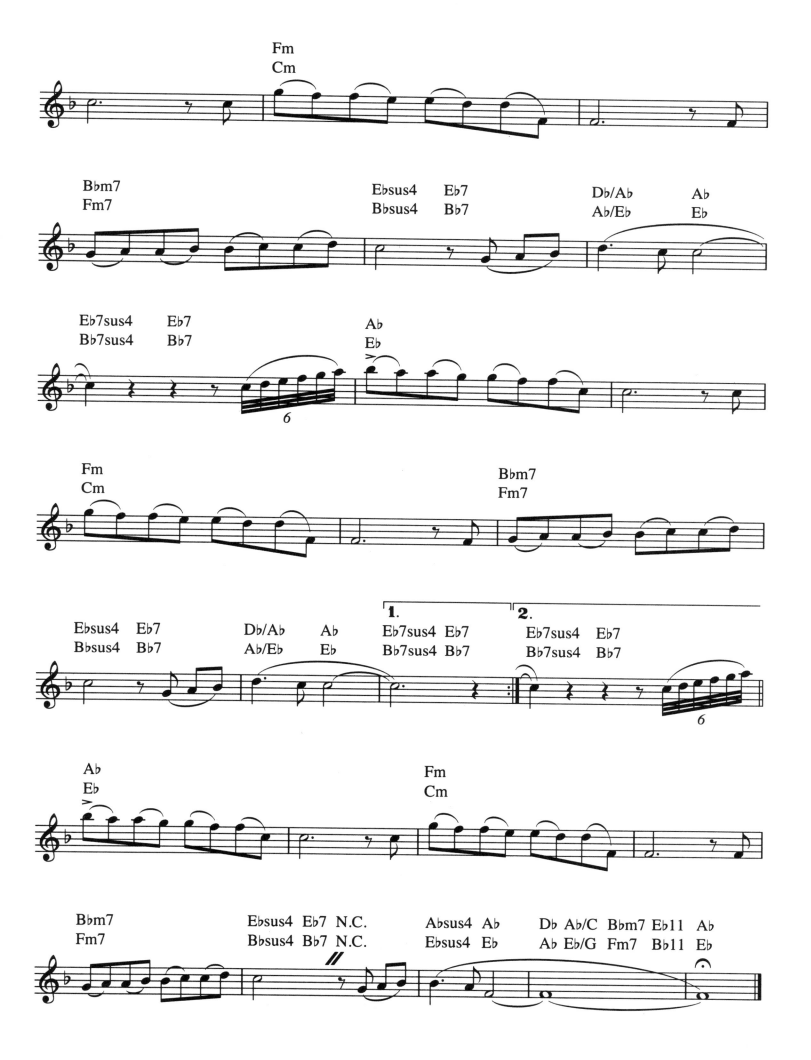

Somewhere In Time

By John Barry

Medium slow (♩ = 80)

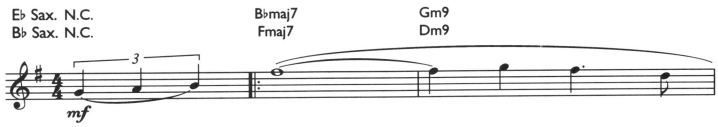

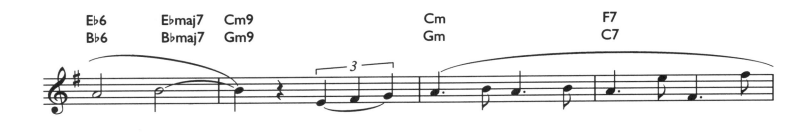

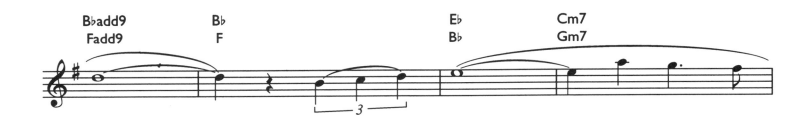

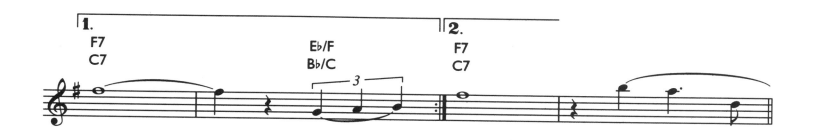
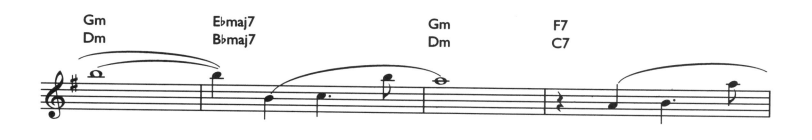

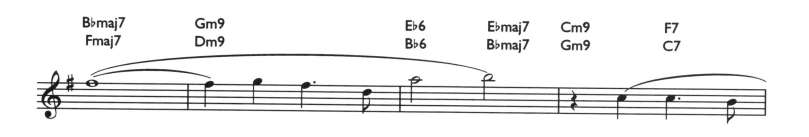
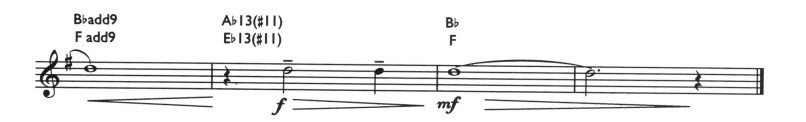

Strangers In The Night

Words by Charles Singleton & Eddie Snyder
Music by Bert Kaempfert

Medium slow

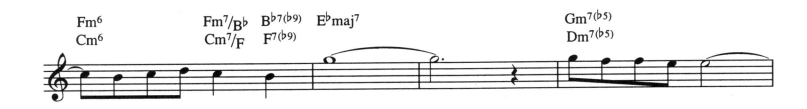

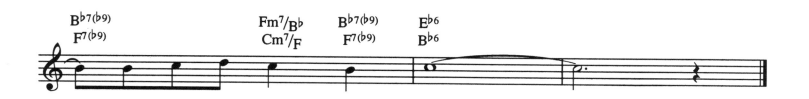

Stars Fell On Alabama

Words by Mitchell Parish
Music by Frank Perkins

Teach Me Tonight

Music by Gene De Paul
Lyrics by Sammy Cahn

Wonderful Tonight

Words & Music by Eric Clapton

rall.